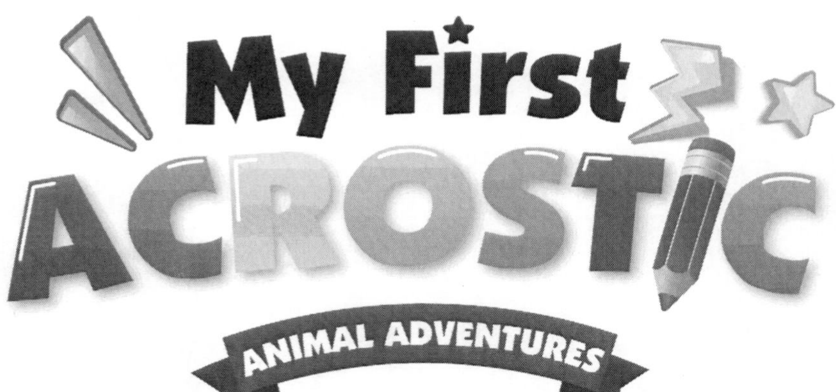

Poetry Gems

Edited By Daisy Job

First published in Great Britain in 2020 by:

Young Writers
Remus House
Coltsfoot Drive
Peterborough
PE2 9BF
Telephone: 01733 890066
Website: www.youngwriters.co.uk

Book Design by Ashley Janson

Softback ISBN 978-1-83928-935-4

Printed and bound in the UK by BookPrintingUK
Website: www.bookprintinguk.com
YB0442F

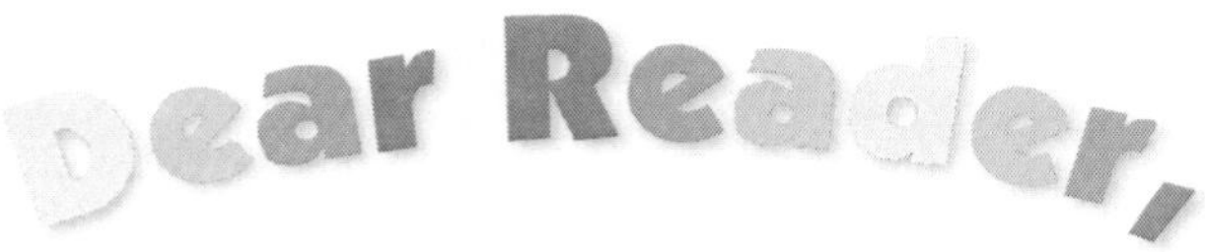

Dear Reader,

Welcome to a fun-filled book of acrostic poems!

Here at Young Writers, we are delighted to introduce our new poetry competition for KS1 pupils, *My First Acrostic: Animal Adventures*. Acrostic poems are an enjoyable way to introduce pupils to the world of poetry and allow the young writer to open their imagination to a range of topics of their choice. The colourful and engaging entry forms allowed even the youngest (or most reluctant) of pupils to create a poem using the acrostic technique and with that, encouraged them to include other literary techniques such as similes and description. Here at Young Writers we are passionate about introducing the love and art of creative writing to the next generation and we love being a part of their journey.

From the jungle to the ocean, pets to mythical monsters, these pupils take you on a journey through the animal kingdom and showcase their budding creativity along the way. So we invite you to dive into these pages and take a glimpse into these blossoming young writers' minds. We hope you will relish these roarsome poems as much as we have.

Contents

Evie Murray (5) 129
Alana (7) 130
Aria Webb (6) 131
Jack Spear (5) 132
Emily Yakub (5) 133
Felix Goodchild (6) 134
Ava McFawn (7) 135
Henry Hayes (6) 136
Harriet Moon (7) 137
Oscar Wright (6) 138
Bethany Savage-Brookes (5) 139
Millie Bayfield (5) 140
Cooper Horn (7) 141
Kiki Thomas (6) 142
Archer Gray (6) 143
Zak Ricketts (5) 144
Mai Bartholomew (6) 145
Shamia-Rose Tade (6) 146
Leo Van Leeuwen (6) 147
Logan Tier (6) 148

St Joseph's Catholic Primary School, Upminster

Emilia Hooper (7) 149
Thea Mai Bishop-Bixby (6) 150
Mary Sullivan (6) 152
Ashley Mathew (7) 153
Matilda Bradley (6) 154
Flynn Nicholls (6) 155
Sophie Edwards (6) 156
Lara Rumble (7) 157
Myah Jerome-Marcellin (6) 158
Oliver Carey (7) 159
Frankie Pettigrew (7) 160
Grace Headley (7) 161
Luke O'Brien (7) 162
Jessica Church (7) 163
Thomas Gray (7) 164
Oliver Richardson-Ojok (6) 165
Clara Callaghan (6) 166
Evie Lafferty (6) 167
Betsy Peck (7) 168
Arthur Hynes (7) 169
Niamh O'Sullivan (6) 170
Ava Bergin (6) 171
Penelope Cross (6) 172
Dylan Jozwiak (6) 173
Chloe Harris (6) 174

The Poems

Elephants

E lephants trumpet loud and long
L ive in Africa
E normous mammals with tusks
P lants are their favourite food
H erds of elephants look after each other
A frican elephants have large ears
N ot light but heavy and strong
T runks to eat and drink
S ee them on safari.

Laila Latimer (6)
Bowdon Preparatory School For Girls, Altrincham

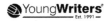

Jaguar For Tea

J ewels for eyes, shine bright like stars
A jaguar can run as fast as a car
G reat big paws pad along the jungle ground
U nique rosettes of black spots can be found
A nd I should point out, while they are beautiful to see
R eally, I would not invite a jaguar for tea.

Gracie O'Brien (6)
Bowdon Preparatory School For Girls, Altrincham

Elephant

E lephants are big
L ovely elephants which I like
E lephants have long trunks
P lants they like to eat
H ave you seen one ever so white?
A n African white elephant
N ot many are left in the wild
T errible people kill them for their tusks.

Kruthi Maharajan (5)
Bowdon Preparatory School For Girls, Altrincham

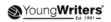

Ooh, Ahh, Aah, Aah!

M ost are very cheeky
O ften brown and hairy
N ever sit still as they love playing
K ing of the trees who can't stop swinging
E njoy eating bananas, seeds and leaves
Y ou will want to watch them for hours!

Bea Burton (5)
Bowdon Preparatory School For Girls, Altrincham

Flamingo

F lamingos have fabulous
L ong legs
A nd a lovely, long neck
M ost flamingos are pink
I love flamingos
N o animal is as pink
G o and find a flamingo
O h my goodness, I love flamingos.

Luna Gonzalez (5)
Bowdon Preparatory School For Girls, Altrincham

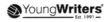

Monkey

M onkeys being naughty
O rangutans swinging in the trees
N oises everywhere
K oalas munching and crunching leaves
E verything is green
Y ellow sky warming the ground.

Clara Mitchell (6)
Bowdon Preparatory School For Girls, Altrincham

Elephant

E normous and gentle
L oving and kind
E xtraordinary to see
P ointy tusks
H airy and huge
A frican and Indian
N aughty but nice
T wisty trunk.

Olivia Ward (6)
Bowdon Preparatory School For Girls, Altrincham

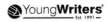

Tiger

T earing meat with its sharp teeth
I n the tall grass, it slowly creeps
G rowling at its next feast
E ver happy in the wild
R oaring tiger, fierce tiger.

Shivani Sinha (6)
Bowdon Preparatory School For Girls, Altrincham

Panda

P andas are cute
A nd cuddly too
N ice and friendly
D on't hurt other animals that live in the tree
A nice bamboo treat after a busy day.

Tanvi Morar (5)
Bowdon Preparatory School For Girls, Altrincham

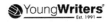

The Hunting Tiger

T he tiger is big and bold
I n the jungle, he hunts
G etting ready to pounce on his prey
E ating food with his cubs
R oar! His tummy is full.

Safiyah Amin (6)
Bowdon Preparatory School For Girls, Altrincham

The Scary Dinosaur

D anger
I n the olden days
N othing is as scary as them
O nly they are scary
S tomp around their world
A re fierce
U nderstand roaring
R *oar, roar, roar!*

Logan Fulbirg (7)
Collingwood Primary School, North Shields

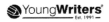

Cute Guinea Pig

G iant guinea pigs
U nderwater submarines
I ncredible
N ike is the best
E mily
A pples are tasty

P eppa Pig
I ncredible
G iant elephants.

William Fred (6)
Collingwood Primary School, North Shields

Monkey

M onkeys love bananas
O ther animals eat monkeys
N o monkeys eat other animals
K ind and cheeky monkeys
E xcellent at stunts
Y ellow bananas are the monkeys'
favourite.

John Davison (7)
Collingwood Primary School, North Shields

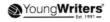

Perfect Penguin

P laying in the icy sea
E xcited about fish
N ever run
G oing swimming every day
U nder the belly sits the egg
I ce is for sliding on
N ot able to fly.

Lilly Cawley (7)
Collingwood Primary School, North Shields

All About Chickens

C hickens live in farms
H atching from egg
I nto cute chick
C an't fly high
K eep themselves warm
E ats seeds
N ever eat the egg.

Oscar Ni (6)
Collingwood Primary School, North Shields

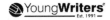

Perfect Parrot

P ink, the parrot is pink
A round the sky it flies
R oams the sky
R eally colourful
O ther birds are boring
T he other birds are rubbish.

Millie Grace (6)

Collingwood Primary School, North Shields

The Funny Panda

P andas are funny
A nd they eat bamboo
N ot very strong
D on't like their size
A nd a bit cheeky.

Ben Ryland (7)
Collingwood Primary School, North Shields

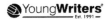

Panda

P andas eat bamboo
A panda lives in a forest
N ever runs
D oes climb on bamboo
A lways snoozing.

Lorenzo Holdaway (7)
Collingwood Primary School, North Shields

Snake

S lither a lot and slither on tall trees
N asty, naughty things eating other
nocturnal animals
A ll the things it eats are living creatures
K illing other animals by biting
E ating other things that are nocturnal
S tealthily looking if you come near.

Amelia (6)
Copthorne Community Infant School, Alfreton

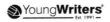

Sloth

S lowly munching the green neon leaves
L ong and deep in the jungle, up tall trees
O nce a week, they go down to the ground
to have a poo
T hey live alone in the tall, dark trees
H alf-deaf and half-blind.

Chloe Imogen Start (6)
Copthorne Community Infant School, Alfreton

Sloth

S lowly, they move up the beautiful tree
L ive in rainforests, they eat light green leaves
O nce a week, they poo on the ground
T wo-toed and three-toed, they can be families
H alf-deaf and half-blind.

Leightan-Jem Cooper (7)
Copthorne Community Infant School, Alfreton

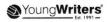

Snake

S lowly, something green slithered through the dark forest
N ecks are long with patterns on
A ll of them have different colours and patterns
K ills small animals like mice
E ats carnivores and meat.

Louie Brown (7)
Copthorne Community Infant School, Alfreton

Snake

S lowly, they slither underneath the dark brown leaves
N ecks are long to catch their prey
A s quick as a wild cat in the rainforest
K ills small mice and white rats
E ats big white rats and mice.

Kaleb Asling (6)

Copthorne Community Infant School, Alfreton

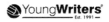

Tiger

T hin white whiskers, I have so animals notice me
I n my powerful jaws I chew animals
G reatest animal you would ever see
E yes are as scary as a snake's
R eally amazing to see in the jungle.

Olivia-Rose (7)
Copthorne Community Infant School, Alfreton

Sloth

S lowly, they move whilst eating the green leaves
L ong claws help them climb the wooden trees
O nce a week, they poo on the ground
T hey are good swimmers
H alf-deaf and half-blind.

Richie Dorning (6)
Copthorne Community Infant School, Alfreton

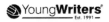

Sloth

S lowly, it moves very sneakily
L eaves don't fall down on the ground
O nce a week, they poo on the ground
T rees have wavy branches
H ave grey and brown fur.

Nikita (6)
Copthorne Community Infant School, Alfreton

Parrot

P retty colours, pink and yellow
A bove the trees, they glide
R ed, shiny wings
R eally loud squawk
O range, curved beak
T hey live for eighty years.

Maci-Rai Tebbitts (7)
Copthorne Community Infant School, Alfreton

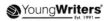

Sloth

S lowly eat bright green leaves
L eaves are scrumptious to eat
O nce a week, they poo on the ground
T all trees to swing on
H alf-deaf and half-blind.

Chloe T (7)
Copthorne Community Infant School, Alfreton

Sloth

S harp claws to help them climb
L ive in rainforest and trees
O nce a week, they poo on the ground
T hey are brown and grey
H alf-deaf and half-blind.

Ella-Rose Armstrong (7)
Copthorne Community Infant School, Alfreton

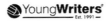

Sloth

S lowly moving through the jungle
L onely, munching leaves
O nce a week, they poo on the ground
T hey are good swimmers
H alf-deaf, half-blind.

Harry Booth (7)
Copthorne Community Infant School, Alfreton

Sloth

S lowly munching on leaves
L ive alone and eat alone
O nce a week, they poo on the ground
T hey are good swimmers
H alf-deaf and half-blind.

Jacob Fulcher (6)
Copthorne Community Infant School, Alfreton

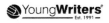

Snake

S cary, red, bright eyes
N ipping with sharp teeth
A creature with no legs
K ills with venom
E xcellent swimmers.

Finley Stevenson-Coxhead (6)
Copthorne Community Infant School, Alfreton

Bear

B rown, thick fur
E at raw meat
A nd they eat mice
R oar really loudly and scarily.

Joshua Wilmott (6)
Copthorne Community Infant School, Alfreton

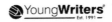

Penguin

P enguins live in Antarctica. Penguins like to
E at snow. Penguins sleep all the time.
N aughty penguins splashing in the water.
G loomy cave is so scary for the penguins
U sing their flippers to swim
I n Antarctica penguins eat fish
N ot leaving their chicks alone!

Piotr Klamka (6)
Huish Primary School, Huish

Giraffes

G iraffes jumping through the grass
I n the African Savannah
R unning around rioting through the plains
A mazing giraffes running into the grass
F ollowing the herd
F antastically exploring in the wild
E legantly roaming the grasslands.

Vaya Worbey (6)
Huish Primary School, Huish

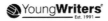

Owls Are Wise

O wls are cute
W ow!
L ove, love, love!
S ort of bird

A little bit big
R ush in the night
E la was an owl in a nursery

W ise owl
I n the dark
S aw a person
E nd of the poem!

Ela Wysocka (6)
Huish Primary School, Huish

Unicorns

U nicorns come out at Christmas
N ight is dark, stars are shining bright
I wish I had a unicorn with wings
C ute as a kitten
O ut into the magical land
R ushing through the stars
N ice as snow
S o, that is my day.

Evie Cattle (5)
Huish Primary School, Huish

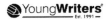

Horses

H orses are really fast, as dashing as can be
O h imagine all the things horses can do?
R eally, really fast as can be
S oaring as quickly as a gazelle
E legantly as quick as a dash they run
S ight is amazing as can be.

Fleur Pollard (5)
Huish Primary School, Huish

Dinosaurs

D inosaurs are fierce
I n the jungle
N o one likes to go near them!
O n their way home
S ome go and hunt down some rivers
A lways eating
U ntil one has found a human!
R un, run away!

Seth Elswood (6)
Huish Primary School, Huish

Jaguars

J aguars are brown and white
A master at prancing!
G reat at roaring!
U sually hard to see
A jaguar is a big cat
R oar, roar, roar they go!
S o cute when they are cubs.

Caitlin Richardson (5)
Huish Primary School, Huish

Pandas

P andas eat bamboo
A dorable sleeping through the day
N aughty pandas running through the mountains
D ashing through the trees
A mazing pandas running through the green grass.

Jake Sargent (6)
Huish Primary School, Huish

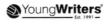

Unicorn

U nicorns are the best pets in the whole wide world
N o wings!
I t is cute
C ute
O ut at night
R eally so kind and pretty
N o one loves unicorns!

Ellie-Jayne McFarlane (5)
Huish Primary School, Huish

Unicorn

U nicorns are cute
N o wings
I n the ice-cold snow
C old winds blow
O n the unicorn is a horn
R un with the unicorn
N obody sees them.

Bella Nathan (6)
Huish Primary School, Huish

Giraffe

G iraffes are cool
I n the hot sun
R un and run
A frica is their home
F ine, long neck
F ine, long legs
E veryone loves giraffes!

Gilbert Kowal (5)
Huish Primary School, Huish

Monkey

M onkeys like swinging
O n the trees
N o going in the water!
K ing monkey
E nd of the forest
Y ellow bananas
S illy and cheeky!

Luca Manley (5)
Huish Primary School, Huish

Dragon

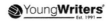

D ragons are fierce and they breathe fire
R oar
A wful and scary
G igantic
O pposite of good, they are horrible
N aughty and dangerous.

Tristan Pearce (5)
Huish Primary School, Huish

Jaguar

J aguars are so fast
A jaguar is a carnivore
G oing to explore
U sing their claws
A jaguar can chase its prey
R eady and waiting.

Isla Storey (5)
Huish Primary School, Huish

Camel

C amels are grumpy all the time
A nimals like them live in the desert
M asters are lazy
E yes are grey
L ong legs
S uper slow!

Jack Wall (6)
Huish Primary School, Huish

Panda

P andas eat bamboo
A panda is black and white
N aughty pandas are cute
D azzling pandas running around
A cheeky panda exploring wildly.

Holly McCarney (6)
Huish Primary School, Huish

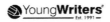

Spider

S piders make webs to catch flies
P eople like spiders
I like spiders!
D own the plughole
E eeek! Spiders!
R un! Run! Run!

Alicja Obrochta (6)
Huish Primary School, Huish

Wolf

W olves are grey
O ff they go to find their food
L aughing and howling as they move
F ollowing their food, stepping slowly on the ground.

Penelope Baker (6)
Huish Primary School, Huish

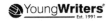

Puppies

P uppies are cute
U p goes my love for puppies
P uppies I love
P uppies are my favourite animals
Y ellow ball for my puppies.

Adele Wheeler (5)
Huish Primary School, Huish

Dragon

D ragons are brave
R oar
A nd it likes sleeping
G et out and scare people
O range dragon
N aughty, evil dragon.

Jayden Veal (5)
Huish Primary School, Huish

Puppy

P uppies run and run
U nder the beds
P uppies can run all day
P eople love dogs and big dogs
Y ummy puppy smell!

Oliver Felstead (5)
Huish Primary School, Huish

Wolf

W olves have sharp teeth
O n trees hunting prey with their claws
L iving in caves and forests
F inishing their dinner up.

Masaki O'Shea (6)

Huish Primary School, Huish

Foxes

F oxes can scream
O ut in the night
X is in vixen
"E ek!" said Dad
"S hhhh!" said Mum.

Elijah Parker (5)
Huish Primary School, Huish

Puppy

P uppies are cute
U pstairs is where they sleep
P uppies are small
P ups like eating shoes!
Y ellow puppy.

Jayden Grayston (6)
Huish Primary School, Huish

Puppy

P retty and cute
U p and down
P uppies are playful
P eople stroke them
Y ou should like them.

Noah McConnell (6)
Huish Primary School, Huish

Cats

C ute and cuddly
A lways sleeping
T iptoe across the roof
S noozing in the sun.

Laura Skrzypczak (5)
Huish Primary School, Huish

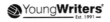

Fantastic Fruit Bats

F ruit bats are blind and nocturnal
R eally loud bats are scared of you
U pside down, bats hang in the deep, dark cave
I love bats!
T he bats are going outside

B ats have wings to help them fly
A nd they eat insects
T he bats need to watch out for bald eagles!

Eleanor Kelsey (5)
Kempsey Primary School, Kempsey

Creepy Crocodile

C rocodiles are very deadly, look out for them!
R eady to eat you
O r could have you for a midnight feast
C reeping to get other animals
O r they eat meat
D eadly, right?
I agree with that
L ook out
E ven when they are sleeping.

Josiah Davies (5)
Kempsey Primary School, Kempsey

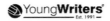

Darting Dart Frog

D art frogs have poison on them
A nd they are black and yellow
R eally good at jumping
T errifying people with their tongues

F rightening flies with their poison
R esting in the trees
O n the move
G ood at jumping over fences.

Cameron Buckley (6)
Kempsey Primary School, Kempsey

Giant Tarantula

T arantulas are scary
A tarantula is poisonous
R eally slow and really venomous
A tarantula is deadly
N o touching the tarantula
T hey are poisonous
U nfriendly tarantula
L egs are very soft
A lways be careful.

Harley Blanden (6)
Kempsey Primary School, Kempsey

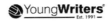

What Snakes Do And Why We Can't Touch Them

S lithery snakes slither
N o touching because they are venomous
A re not friendly because they might bite you
K eep away from snakes because they are venomous
E xtraordinary animals!

Rosa Murray (6)
Kempsey Primary School, Kempsey

Jumping Jaguars

J aguars
A re spotty
G reedy and eat meat
U sually very fierce
A nd they have really sharp claws
R un really fast.

Zachary Hope (6)

Kempsey Primary School, Kempsey

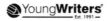

Jumping Jaguar

J aguars are fast
A nd jaguars are deadly
G o on a hunt
U p a tall tree
A nd they are thieves
R un to his home.

Johnny Allonby (6)
Kempsey Primary School, Kempsey

Jumpy Jaguars

J aguars are very sneaky
A nd stealthy
G ot a lot of energy
U nkind
A nd frightening
R un very quickly.

Hanna Nalepa (6)
Kempsey Primary School, Kempsey

Slow Sloth

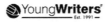

S loths are slow
L aid back on trees
O ff the trees, they hang
T he sloth sees a toucan
H e is free.

Elsa Sampson (5)
Kempsey Primary School, Kempsey

Unicorn

U nicorns are beautiful and magical too
N o unicorns have wings, only the baby unicorns
I n the unicorn land, live the most beautiful unicorns
C an feed one of the unicorns
O n the hill, there was treasure
R unning up the hill, the unicorn went
N ena was a little unicorn.

Emilia Strong (6)
Nettlesworth Primary School, Nettlesworth

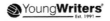

Serpent

S omething is lurking in the dungeon
E verything like rats are eaten!
R azor-sharp teeth, it's a serpent!
P ressure it puts on its prey
E verything is bones!
N asty snakes are big, big, big!
T asty meals you would make for the
serpent!

Praim Bassi (7)
Nettlesworth Primary School, Nettlesworth

Snow Wolf

S now wolves are fast
N o one can catch them
O nly fast people can catch them
W hite and floaty they are

W hiskers are sharp
O nly wolves can eat meat
L ots of wolves are vicious
F ast and fierce they are.

Charlie John Whittington (6)
Nettlesworth Primary School, Nettlesworth

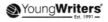

Unicorn

U ntil magic goes away
N ormally, the unicorn eats grass
I n a unicorn, there is magic
C an it fly?
O range unicorns
R un as fast as they can
N ormally, they are beautiful.

Lara Redpath (6)
Nettlesworth Primary School, Nettlesworth

Unicorn

U nicorns are pretty
N ow, unicorns don't exist
I love unicorns
C olourful unicorns
O nly unicorns can fly
R eally pretty unicorns
N ew unicorns are coming.

Sophia Logan (7)
Nettlesworth Primary School, Nettlesworth

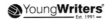

Zebra

Z oo, the zebra, is in the zoo
E ach day the zebra has a poo
B lack and white are zebra stripes
R eal zebras are alive right now
A ll zebras eat the same.

Millie Joyce Barron (7)
Nettlesworth Primary School, Nettlesworth

T-Rex

T he T-rex has got massive teeth

R unning as fast as he can to catch his prey
E veryone likes the T-rex
X -ray vision he has.

Matthew Boden (6)
Nettlesworth Primary School, Nettlesworth

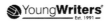

Pretty Penguins

P enguins
E at
N ice fish
G o
U nderwater
I n the snow at
N ight-time.

Jasleen Bassi (4)
Nettlesworth Primary School, Nettlesworth

T-Rex

T he T-rex is eating a triceratops

R unning as fast as he can
E ating meat
X -ray vision.

Hassan Khalil (6)
Nettlesworth Primary School, Nettlesworth

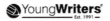

Dogs

D ogs are cute and fluffy
O r snuggly
G reat, aren't they?
S o, do you want one?

Charlie Jack Rendall (6)
Nettlesworth Primary School, Nettlesworth

Uni Unicorns

U nbelievable
N ice
I cy
C ool
O n
R ainbow
N ow.

Isabella Robson (4)
Nettlesworth Primary School, Nettlesworth

Cat

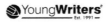

C ats are fluffy
A cat is sitting on the couch
T he cat tidied the house.

Ava Parkin (6)
Nettlesworth Primary School, Nettlesworth

Harriet Horse

H orse
O n the
R ace track
S ports
E vent.

Imogen Flowers (5)

Nettlesworth Primary School, Nettlesworth

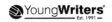

Chick, Chick, Chicken

C ute
H atchling
I nside
C hick
K issing.

Alana Lloyd (5)
Nettlesworth Primary School, Nettlesworth

Dog

D ogs are cute
O ften, dogs eat bones
G ood dogs are trained.

Freddie Atkins (6)
Nettlesworth Primary School, Nettlesworth

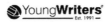

Furry Fox

F uzzy tail
O range, fluffy fur
e X plores in the forest.

Florence S (4)
Nettlesworth Primary School, Nettlesworth

Cat

C ats are cute
A ll cats are furry
T he cat likes milk.

Sam Ellis Jamieson (6)
Nettlesworth Primary School, Nettlesworth

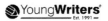

Cat

C ats are furry
A ll cats are soft
T hey get fish.

Olivia Smith (5)
Nettlesworth Primary School, Nettlesworth

Crabs

C rabby
R ascal
A nimal
B ites.

Archie Richardson (5)
Nettlesworth Primary School, Nettlesworth

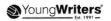

Dizzy Dogs

D ashing
O range
G herkin.

Harry Showler (5)
Nettlesworth Primary School, Nettlesworth

Crazy Cats

C heetahs
A ttack
T igers.

Oscar Corker (4)
Nettlesworth Primary School, Nettlesworth

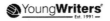

Cutie Cat

C ute
A nd
T ickly.

Oliver Whittington (4)
Nettlesworth Primary School, Nettlesworth

Dinosaur

D inosaurs walked Earth for 165 million years
I saw dinosaur bones when I was four
N o dinosaurs are still alive
O n the Earth, the dinosaurs died
S pinosauri were the biggest carnivores
A diplodocus was a herbivore
U nder the ground, there are dinosaur bones
R oaring at other dinosaurs.

Callum Glasgow (6)
Oakwood Primary School, Glasgow

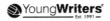

Dinosaurs

D inosaurs walked the Earth for 165 million years
I know dinosaurs are extinct
N o dinosaurs are alive
O n Monday, I went to see a movie about dinosaurs
S kin so hard
A re they good or bad?
U nder volcanoes, they look for food
R oaring at the sky
S noring on the ground.

Shanade Duncan (6)
Oakwood Primary School, Glasgow

Dinosaurs

D inosaurs walked over the Earth for 165 million years
I saw dinosaurs that died in a film
N o dinosaurs are alive
O n Earth, they are extinct
S ome dinosaurs have spikes on their backs
A re dangerous
U nder volcanoes
R oaring at the birds in the sky
S harp claws.

Ben McDonald (6)
Oakwood Primary School, Glasgow

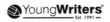

Unicorns

U nicorns have magical powers
N o unicorns are alive
I like big, beautiful unicorns
C ute, colourful horns
O ver the
R ainbow, they go
N ice long tails
S uper cool wings.

Joyce Huang (6)
Oakwood Primary School, Glasgow

Dolphins

D olphins have clever brains
O ver the waves, they swim
L ive in the sea
P eople see them going up and down
H appy dolphins see each other
I n the water
N ever are sad.

Jessica Bell (6)
Oakwood Primary School, Glasgow

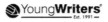

Unicorns

U nicorns have magical powers
N ot real
I n a book
C an fly
O ver the castle
R iding in the sky
N ever want humans to fly on them
S parkles on their horns.

Darcy Twigg (6)
Oakwood Primary School, Glasgow

Spiders

S piders are very venomous
P eople don't like them
I 'm not scared of them
D ie in their web
E ight legs
R un down the wall
S piders bite other people.

Kai Moffat (7)
Oakwood Primary School, Glasgow

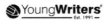

Unicorns

U nicorns have magical powers
N ice horns
I love unicorns
C ute as a butterfly
O n a cloud
R ainbow tail
N ever sad.

Ava Anderson (6)
Oakwood Primary School, Glasgow

Birds

B irds have feathers
I like birds
R obins are red
D inner is worms
S itting on a branch.

Yusrah Farheen (6)
Oakwood Primary School, Glasgow

Lions

L ions sleep all day
I n the jungle
O ver the jungle
N ever eat grass
S itting on a rock.

Olivia McNeil (5)
Oakwood Primary School, Glasgow

Shark

S harp teeth
H as a big fin
A lways hunts for food
R ace each other
K ing of the sea.

Jamie Musgrave (6)
Oakwood Primary School, Glasgow

Whale

W hales are big
H ave a big tail
A lways in the sea
L ong tail
E normous.

Le Xuan Chen (6)
Oakwood Primary School, Glasgow

Sheep

S oft
H as wool
E ats grass
E very day
P lays in a field.

Marc Haldane (7)
Oakwood Primary School, Glasgow

Dog

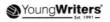

D ogs are big
O range dogs run away
G rowling at people.

Charlie Willows (6)
Oakwood Primary School, Glasgow

Pigs

P igs are pink
I t lives on a farm
G reedy for food.

Erleen Irwin (6)
Oakwood Primary School, Glasgow

Cat

C ats drink milk
A nd eat
T hen they sleep all day.

Oscar McNeil (5)
Oakwood Primary School, Glasgow

Unicorn Magic

U nicorns are my favourite magical animal,
they only eat candy corn
N o one at all knows where they are born
I t is said their power is truth and they
pierce the heart of a liar with their horn
C an you believe their horn is three metres
long?
O ther people don't believe in unicorns but
they are wrong
R eally they are everywhere: in your
dreams, at the end of rainbows, they're
where you want them to be
N ever have I seen such a beautiful
creature. I promise, look around and you
will see.

Erin Bendell (7)

Purbrook Infant School, Purbrook

Unicorn Dreams

U nder the sun and the old apple trees
N ear the fields where the lambs run free
I dream of the fairies who come out to play
C hasing all of my problems away
O ver meadows and fields as we leap and run
R ainbows show up and we have such fun
N ow it's time to go home and as we say goodbye
S tars are starting to show in the sky.

Evie Maxwell (6)
Purbrook Infant School, Purbrook

Swimming Swordfish

S wordfish have swords on their faces
W hen it swims, it blows bubbles
O cean is where they like to live
R acing through the water at fifty miles per hour
D id you know that we eat swordfish?
F emales are bigger than males
I have never seen a swordfish
S illy swordfish would go in front of predators
H ello swordfish.

Alistair Hutchin (6)
Purbrook Infant School, Purbrook

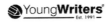

My Kitten Cece

K ittens are soft, furry and fluffy
I nviting you to rub their tummy
T oys are one of her favourite things
T hey are full of energy and daring. Cece likes climbing up curtains!
E very day I give Cece cuddles and she loves it because she purrs
N aughty Tortie is her nickname but I love her still the same!

Grace Barber (6)
Purbrook Infant School, Purbrook

Hippopotamus

H airy chin
I nteresting tongue
P arping bottom
P rickly belly
O pen jaws
P ointy ears
O range and melon smasher
T eeth like a knife
A mazing strength
M ore blubber than rhinos
U nbelievably heavy
S top killing hippos!

Noah Powell (6)
Purbrook Infant School, Purbrook

Small, Fluffy, Hungry Owl

F luffy is my name. I am an owl. I have
R eally big eyes and my best friend is a cow
I am shy so I hide away in the day and I really
E njoy cuddles and snuggling in hay. I love
N ight-time, that's when I come out to play. It's my
D inner time when I catch my prey.

Maddison Haynes (6)
Purbrook Infant School, Purbrook

Dog's Kisses

D ogs are furry
O ften they lick people
G ives lots of kisses
S oft and warm to touch

K ids love dogs
I like their fur
S niffing and running
S lobbering and chasing
E xcited and happy
S ausage dogs are the best.

Grace Egginton (6)
Purbrook Infant School, Purbrook

My Lily Cat

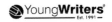

M y little Lily
Y ellow fur, she has

L ily has brown eyes
I give her cuddles
L ily plays with a ball
Y ellow sun makes Lily bright

C ute and quiet pet
A fish and milk, she eats
T alks with meow sounds.

Noursine Khamellah (6)
Purbrook Infant School, Purbrook

Unicorn

U nicorns are always happy
N ever are they sad
I ce creams are my favourite
C uddles are the best
O ur coat is soft and shiny and stands out from the rest
R ainbow sparkles bring so much fun
N ever is a unicorn's work done.

Keira Seymour (6)
Purbrook Infant School, Purbrook

Big Five

L ikes to climb trees
E yes are scary
O ne of the big five has pointy ears
P aws have sharp claws
A frican and Asia are my home
R uns at a speed of thirty-six miles per hour
D ark spots on my body called rosettes.

Oliver Austin-Jones (5)
Purbrook Infant School, Purbrook

Meerkat

M eerkats are very cute
E ating lots of yucky things
E ating reptiles and bugs
R unning and burrowing in the desert
K eeping safe in a mob or a gang
A lways standing tall
T hey chatter noisily to each other.

Ava Yakub (5)
Purbrook Infant School, Purbrook

Where Are My Friends?

U nder a rainbow
N iamh calls for her friends
I wonder where they are?
C alling, "Come back friends."
O ver the hill they are eating
R un home as fast as you can
N ow, it's party time.

Matilda Ramsell (5)
Purbrook Infant School, Purbrook

Lovely Horses

H ay for my dinner and to keep me warm at night
O utside I can trot and gallop
R iding with my owner and having a lovely time
S leeping in my stable after a long, busy day
E normous teeth are great for chewing.

Leo Walsh (6)
Purbrook Infant School, Purbrook

Narwhal

N avigate to find food
A rctic is their home
R ange from thirteen feet to eighteen feet
W hite whales
H ave a special horn
A rctic fish, they love to eat
L ike a unicorn.

Grace Morris (6)
Purbrook Infant School, Purbrook

The Elephant

E normous ears
L ong trunk
E ating green leaves
P laying in the water
H eavy animal
A frica is their home
N early as big as a bus
T usks that are sharp.

Flynn Brutnell (5)
Purbrook Infant School, Purbrook

Sunshine Horse

H orses are my favourite
O ften, I would see them
R unning through the fields
S eeing them makes me happy
E ven when I'm sad
S o horses are so special - especially to me.

Maddison Reid Robins (6)
Purbrook Infant School, Purbrook

The Magic Unicorn

U p high into the sky
N ight-time, flying high
I saw a sparkly unicorn
C louds as soft as candyfloss
O n a winter's night
N ight-night, love the magic unicorn.

Ivy Newcombe (6)
Purbrook Infant School, Purbrook

Unicorn

U nicorns are magical
N ice and soft
I love unicorns
C olourful bodies
O ne horn on their head
R arely seen and sparkly
N obody knows where they live.

Phoebe McNiff (6)
Purbrook Infant School, Purbrook

Unicorn

U nicorns are glittery
N ice and shiny
I love how they sparkle
C olourful and sweet
O h, how pretty
R unning in the woods
N ow, they are having fun.

Emma Jarrett (5)
Purbrook Infant School, Purbrook

Lion King

L oud roars
I n Africa
O n top of the food chain
N ever afraid

K ing of beasts
I n the night, hunting
N ice mane
G rrr, stay away.

Devon Netting (6)
Purbrook Infant School, Purbrook

Slow Little Sloth

S low is the only way they go
L ife in the rainforest is all they know
O nce a week they have a poo
T hey are very smart
H anging upside down, is that a clue?

Marlie-Anne Byrne (6)
Purbrook Infant School, Purbrook

Elephant

E ars that are flappy
L ong trunk
E mpathetic
P illar-like legs
H erbivore
A thick skin
N ever forgets
T usks.

Joseph Murray (6)
Purbrook Infant School, Purbrook

Monkey

M onkeys swing
O ver the jungle
N ever missing a branch
K eeping fit, keep your
E yes open for bananas
Y eah, I have my bananas now.

Evie Murray (5)
Purbrook Infant School, Purbrook

Elephants

E normous
L ong trunk
E ats bushes
P owerful
H ealthy
A dventurous
N on-stop
T houghtful
S haring.

Alana (7)
Purbrook Infant School, Purbrook

Lioness

L ions hunting
I t is a queen
O nly girl lions hunt
N ala from The Lion King
E xpert hunter
S neaky
S ee them in Africa.

Aria Webb (6)
Purbrook Infant School, Purbrook

Kittens

K ittens play
I n a box
T oday, my kittens played in the garden
T omorrow, he will
E at pasta
N ot fish
S illy kitten.

Jack Spear (5)
Purbrook Infant School, Purbrook

Tiger

T igers are furry
I n the Indian jungle
G athering food in an ambush
E ating lots of meat
R oaring loudly
S leeping in the sun.

Emily Yakub (5)
Purbrook Infant School, Purbrook

Meaty T-Rex

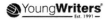

T he tyrant lizard king

R eally fierce and big
E veryone is scared of its loud roaring
X -rays show that it eats meat and not a
leafy twig!

Felix Goodchild (6)
Purbrook Infant School, Purbrook

Happy Horse

H appy horses gallop
O lympic equestrian jumping
R iding hats have different silks
S ome horses like to jump
E questrian centres.

Ava McFawn (7)
Purbrook Infant School, Purbrook

Charlie The Crab

C reaking claws that like to nip
R unning sideways very quick
A round rock pools, they like to hide
B athing, waiting for the tide.

Henry Hayes (6)
Purbrook Infant School, Purbrook

The Deer Forest

D elighted, I am running
E nergetically through the vast
E mpty lands, weeds and forests
R ustling branches and leaves as I go.

Harriet Moon (7)
Purbrook Infant School, Purbrook

Dinosaur

D angerous
I nteresting
N aughty
O ld
S cary
A ngry
U nusual
R oar.

Oscar Wright (6)
Purbrook Infant School, Purbrook

Cats

C ats are really furry
A mazing at seeing in the dark
T hey eat cat food and play
S unning themselves all day.

Bethany Savage-Brookes (5)
Purbrook Infant School, Purbrook

Rainbow Dash

U nkind
N aughty
I t's pretty
C olourful
O ne horn
R eally fast
N ice.

Millie Bayfield (5)
Purbrook Infant School, Purbrook

Bear Fun

B ears are fun in the sun
E xciting bears dance around
A ngry when woken from sleep
R oaring for fish.

Cooper Horn (7)
Purbrook Infant School, Purbrook

My Mythical Pegasus

P owerful
E legant
G raceful
A dventurous
S peedy
U nusual
S trong.

Kiki Thomas (6)

Purbrook Infant School, Purbrook

Barn Owl

B rave
A ctive
R ustling
N octurnal

O minous
W hite
L ight.

Archer Gray (6)

Purbrook Infant School, Purbrook

Geoff The Frog

F rogs like to jump
R ibbit ribbit is the sound
O ggly-googly eyes
G reen skin and brown spots.

Zak Ricketts (5)
Purbrook Infant School, Purbrook

Mai's Owl

B ranch
A ctive
R at
N est

O ld
W ise
L arge.

Mai Bartholomew (6)
Purbrook Infant School, Purbrook

Penguin

P enguin
E ggs
N est
G rey
U nique
I ce
N oisy.

Shamia-Rose Tade (6)
Purbrook Infant School, Purbrook

Lion Needs A Friend

L oudly he roars
I t frightens everybody
O ff they all run
N ow he's lonely.

Leo Van Leeuwen (6)
Purbrook Infant School, Purbrook

Bat

B ats are awesome
A nd they hunt at night
T ired bats sleep at night.

Logan Tier (6)
Purbrook Infant School, Purbrook

Meerkats

M eerkats are my favourite thing, they are very cheeky
E ating spiders, snakes and lizards, they have to be very sneaky
E very meerkat has good eyesight
R unning through the desert until the eagles give them a fright
K eeping safe out in the wild
A lways looking out for their child
T wisting, turning, digging with their claws
S and is moving in-between their paws.

Emilia Hooper (7)
St Joseph's Catholic Primary School, Upminster

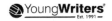

The Giant Panda

G iant pandas are part of the bear family
I t has a black and white coat with black patches around its eyes
A iluropoda melanoleuca is the scientific name for the giant panda
N ative to China, pandas live in the mountains
T ree climbing is one of a panda's favourite things to do

P andas do not hibernate like other bears
A panda's paw has six digits, it uses them to hold bamboo
N o other bears have the same eyes as a giant panda
D iet of a panda is made almost entirely of bamboo

A ll they do is eat and eat and eat and rest and rest and rest and rest
S ometimes they can eat up to sixteen hours a day!

Thea Mai Bishop-Bixby (6)
St Joseph's Catholic Primary School, Upminster

Penny The Elephant

E xcellent elephants in a
L ine. All
E xcept one
P enny was her name, she was only young
H iding behind the rock because something
was wrong with her tongue!
A nd all the other elephants shouted out
her
N ame and lifted up their
T runks! They wanted to play a game
S quirting water out of their trunks, Penny
wanted to play the same!

Mary Sullivan (6)
St Joseph's Catholic Primary School, Upminster

Dolphins

D olphins swimming in the shimmering blue sea
O ctopuses and otters swim around her elegantly
L ower down in the deep ocean blue
P ufferfish swim right to you
H appiness holds hands, 100s of memories
I n the dolphin's mind comes melodies
N ever-ending nature bonds us three
S wimming with glee.

Ashley Mathew (7)

St Joseph's Catholic Primary School, Upminster

Cheetah

C ats are very small but not this one
H ave a look at this mammal with sharp
claws and black spots
E ats meat, antelope and gazelle
E asily catches its prey
T he fastest land animal
A frican savannah, grasslands and
mountains are its habitats
H ave you guessed what this animal is yet?
A cheetah!

Matilda Bradley (6)
St Joseph's Catholic Primary School, Upminster

Snow Fox

S lowly, she stumbles around the snow
N ight and day, she has a feisty meal
O ver the mountains, you see her green eyes
W ow, she is so fast and furious

F abulous snow fox, leaping around
O ver the mountains, you can see her ears pop up
X marks the spot where she digs to make her home.

Flynn Nicholls (6)
St Joseph's Catholic Primary School, Upminster

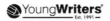

Can You Guess My Animal?

E normous ears and tough tusks
L ong tails and huge trunks
E verything grey and a little bit wrinkly
P lants and bananas they like to eat
H eavy and happy
A nd they never forget
N ow, can you guess my animal?
T hat's right, it's an elephant!

Sophie Edwards (6)
St Joseph's Catholic Primary School, Upminster

Slithery Snake

S ilent, deadly, alarming snakes curled up on a branch
N asty, poisonous snakes using their venom to catch their prey
A ngry snakes, very dangerous, sometimes killing
K iller snake sneaking up on you in a slippery way out of a bush
E ager snakes looking at you in a cunning way.

Lara Rumble (7)
St Joseph's Catholic Primary School, Upminster

Delightful Dolphin

D elightful dolphins swim elegantly across
the deep blue sea
O ver and under the crashing waves
L oudly squeaking with her family
P eople smile and cheer
H igh leaps through the loops
I n excitement and joy
N ever failing to please their happy crowd.

Myah Jerome-Marcellin (6)
St Joseph's Catholic Primary School, Upminster

All About Dogs

D ogs are very popular pets with their four legs and waggy tails. They like to play and run.

O ver jumping, overjoyed, they have so much fun. With their clever noses they can search and find, some dogs even help the blind.

G ood dogs running around in the park, playing games until dark.

Oliver Carey (7)

St Joseph's Catholic Primary School, Upminster

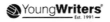

Monkey

M ischievous, playful and loud
O ut in the jungle, sometimes in a troop
N aughty, nibbling bananas as fast as lightning
K een to hang from their powerful tails
E xtremely agile as they swing through the trees
Y es, these primate animals are very cheeky.

Frankie Pettigrew (7)
St Joseph's Catholic Primary School, Upminster

Koala

K now that we care about you, little bear
O h how we love your fluffy, grey hair
A nd your snuggly friends as lovely as you
L ight up our world and our love is so true
A ustralia's trees are where you live, you
are cute, cuddly, clingy and our love we
give.

Grace Headley (7)
St Joseph's Catholic Primary School, Upminster

The Blue Beauty

B elongs in the water
L ives in deep oceans
U nique tummy
E ats krill

W ow, I am so big
H umans and harpoons are my enemies
A n ancient mammal
L ikes travelling around the world
E ndangered species, I am.

Luke O'Brien (7)
St Joseph's Catholic Primary School, Upminster

Giraffe

G iant neck to reach leaves in high trees
I n the zoo for people to see
R un faster than you could imagine
A wake for most of the time
F ur is short, spots so big
F ound in Africa, they survive the heat
E ndangered... please help.

Jessica Church (7)
St Joseph's Catholic Primary School, Upminster

The Very Cheeky Monkey

M onkeys love to swing through the trees
O ver branches in the breeze
N o one sees them because they are sneaky
K een to have some fun, always cheeky!
E ating bananas and other fruit
Y ou might even think they're cute.

Thomas Gray (7)
St Joseph's Catholic Primary School, Upminster

Tigers

T igers are wild, they like to have fun
I n the zoos, they jump and run
G irls and boys come to see them play
E very day they are locked away
R eally, they should be left to roam
S afe in the jungle, where they call home.

Oliver Richardson-Ojok (6)
St Joseph's Catholic Primary School, Upminster

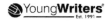

Dashing Dogs

D ashing dogs all over the place
O n the streets, in the park, even on my comfy bed
G iant ones, small ones, spotty ones, making lots of noise, getting in my ears
S ome are black and some are white, they are setting off to their homes tonight.

Clara Callaghan (6)
St Joseph's Catholic Primary School, Upminster

Dogs

D ogs like to run and play with their owners every day
O n the hill, far away, they bark to other dogs every day
G oing in the garden to more trees, wagging their tails on their way
S itting down, standing up, what a cuddly little pup.

Evie Lafferty (6)
St Joseph's Catholic Primary School, Upminster

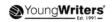

Rhinoceros

R umbling gallops
H umongous body
I n Africa
N early extinct
O ut in the sun
C harging enemies
E ncounters
R oaring noises
O ver the plain
S earching for grass.

Betsy Peck (7)
St Joseph's Catholic Primary School, Upminster

Penguin

P erson-shaped little bird
E ating fish and diving deep
N oisy beaks squawking loud
G ood at keeping warm
U nderwater swimming fast
I nside an egg, they grow
N ever flying in the sky.

Arthur Hynes (7)
St Joseph's Catholic Primary School, Upminster

Playful Pandas

P andas are good climbers
A lot of pandas love running and rolling
N ice pandas adore their babies very much
D ifferent pandas play different games
A lso, playful pandas munch their chewy
bamboo.

Niamh O'Sullivan (6)
St Joseph's Catholic Primary School, Upminster

What Am I?

S low as a slimy slug
L ong claws with only three toes
O h dear me, I am very lazy as can be
T here in the trees, you'll find me hanging around
H ave you guessed what I am?

Ava Bergin (6)
St Joseph's Catholic Primary School, Upminster

Pandamonium

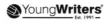

P andas like to play
A nd eat bamboo
N apping is also what they like to do
D o you think that
A pple juice is what pandas like to drink?

Penelope Cross (6)
St Joseph's Catholic Primary School, Upminster

Tilly

T illy is very special to me
I love her so much
L ike a busy bee
L ove her to the moon and back
Y es, this is a true fact.

Dylan Jozwiak (6)
St Joseph's Catholic Primary School, Upminster

Lion

L eader of the jungle
I ndependent animals
O bviously the scariest animal on land
N ever afraid of anything.

Chloe Harris (6)
St Joseph's Catholic Primary School, Upminster

Young Writers Information

We hope you have enjoyed reading this book – and that you will continue to in the coming years.

If you're a young writer who enjoys reading and creative writing, or the parent of an enthusiastic poet or story writer, do visit our website **www.youngwriters.co.uk**. Here you will find free competitions, workshops and games, as well as recommended reads, a poetry glossary and our blog. There's lots to keep budding writers motivated to write!

If you would like to order further copies of this book, or any of our other titles, then please give us a call or order via your online account.

Young Writers
Remus House
Coltsfoot Drive
Peterborough
PE2 9BF
(01733) 890066
info@youngwriters.co.uk

Join in the conversation!
Tips, news, giveaways and much more!